Different is Me!!!

Sandra Grace Walker

Butterfly Language Publishing

ISBN 978-1-7371309-0-1 (Paperback Edition)
ISBN 978-1-7371309-1-8 (Hardcover Edition)
ISBN 978-1-7371309-2-5   (E-book Edition)

Publisher's Cataloging-In-Publication Data
(Prepared by The Donohue Group, Inc.)

Names: Walker, Sandra Grace, author. | White, Sharquita, illustrator.
Title: Different is me!!! / [written by]: Sandra Grace Walker ; [illustrated by: Sharquita White].
Description: Hampstead, MD : Butterfly Language Publishing, [2021] | Interest age level: 003-007. | Summary: "Different is Me, is a picture book showing brown boys how handsome they are in their own skin. This book shows that being different is beautiful just they way you are. It provides positive affirmations of self-love. It celebrates our unique features with the comparisons to nature and our surroundings"--Provided by publisher.
Identifiers: ISBN 9781737130901 (paperback) | ISBN 9781737130918 (hardcover) | ISBN 9781737130925 (ebook)
Subjects: LCSH: African American boys--Juvenile fiction. | Human skin color--Juvenile fiction. | Body image in children--Juvenile fiction. | Individual differences in children--Juvenile fiction. | CYAC: African American boys--Fiction. | Human skin color--Fiction. | Body image--Fiction. | Individual differences--Fiction. | LCGFT: Picture books.
Classification: LCC PZ7.1.W3487 Di 2021 (print) | LCC PZ7.1.W3487 (ebook) | DDC [E]--dc23

Library of Congress Control Number
2021908398

Printed and bound in the United States of America
First printing May 2021

Published by Butterfly Language Publishing
Hampstead, MD 21074
Visit www.butterflylanguagepublishing.com
Butterfly Language Publishing

Dedicated to my Young Kings in
training, Khari and Khaliq.
Continue to flourish into who
God created you to be . Mommy
loves you and always LOVE
YOURSELF!!!

Acknowledgment

Khari you are great beyond words can explain. God created you in the likeness of thee. He designed you especially for me. To show me what love really is, to guide me through the trying years. To teach me to be patient and kind, to love unconditionally until the end of time. Your heart glows bright...you are my sonshine day and night.

Who is that I see, over there looking at me?
Checking me out, seeing what I am about.

Who could that possibly be?

Oh, that's me...

Wow, look at my sun-kissed brown skin.

Toasted to perfection, that beautiful skin I am in.
I am gifted with a complexion to protect me.
Melanin deep within...

So let's see, how is my hair?

Is my hair kinky, curly, or straight?

Short or long?

It doesn't matter because I love them all!

I can braid it, fade it and curl it up...

I am expressing my creativity and that's what's up!

Look at my eyes so bright.
Like the midnight's moonlight.

Gazing into the stars, to a galaxy afar.
There is a twinkle in my eyes, that can not
be disguised.

And my nose fits my face perfectly so...
Like an Egyptian sculpture created by my Ancestors.

The truth is...we are decendants of Kings.

But what about my mouth?
What about my lips?
They are different from what I see,

But they are beautifully shaped like
the ocean and sea.
Full and plump for everyone to see.

A smile so bright it can be seen at night.
A smile goes a long way, I wish that everyone could see that!
It can change your world if you just believe that.
I love my smile it shows that I am proud.
Proud to be ME!

I am not like the other kids I see...

I am different and that is fine with me!!!

Because I LOVE ME!

Tell me what is different about you?
Why do you think it is different?

_____

_____

_____

_____

The image I see starts with ME!!!
Say these reflections everyday and you will feel them in every way.

I am GREAT

I am BRILLANT

I am LOVEABLE

I am KIND

I am STRONG

I am HEALTHY

I am GOOD-LOOKING

And

I am ME.

About the Author ♥

Sandra Grace Walker is a mother of two beautiful boys. She have always loved writing, especially poems. She always kept a journal and when something came to her heart, she would write it down. Sandra thought she wrote poems for herself and she would never share them. She did not know that the love for writing would turn into her writing a children's book. She loves reading to her boys at bedtime and now she can add her book (Different is Me!!!) to their library.

About the Illustrator

Sharquita White is a stay at home mother of three. She has a seven year old daughter, five year old daughter that has Sickle Cell Disease and a two year old son. Her hobbies are drawing and doing crafts.

Lightning Source UK Ltd.
Milton Keynes UK
UKHW050239080621
385087UK00002B/55